"When I went to school my history lessons were all about learning the names of kings and endless lists of dates. *Yawn*. But exciting history asks: How did people live and how did they die? How did they feel? Were they just like us or more like aliens from another planet? Those are the questions that *Battle Books* explore. I wish Gary Smailes and his books had been around when I went to school."
— **Terry Deary, author of** *Horrible Histories*

BATTLE BOOKS

Prepare to fight your own battle...

Start the story, then choose which numbered paragraph to follow. Go to that paragraph to continue on and see if you can help to defeat the Japanese forces holding the island of Iwo Jima.

YOU are a US Marine in the 28th Regiment, 5th Marine Division. You are highly trained, and will be expected to follow orders from senior-ranking marines. You are one man in a 70,000-strong force, armed with a M1 Garand rifle, bayonet and grenades (when you can find them). You are one of the few, one of the proud.

D0320565

US MARINE KIT AND WEAPONS

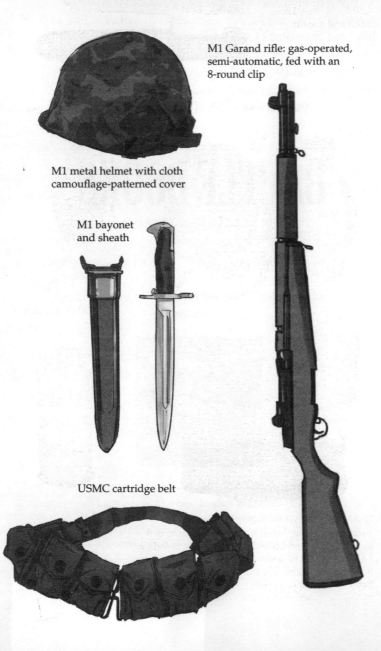

M1 Garand rifle: gas-operated, semi-automatic, fed with an 8-round clip

M1 metal helmet with cloth camouflage-patterned cover

M1 bayonet and sheath

USMC cartridge belt

BATTLE BOOKS

IWO JIMA

Gary Smailes

Illustrated by David Cousens

LONDON•SYDNEY

For Caroline —— G.S.

First published in 2011
by Franklin Watts

Text © Gary Smailes 2011
Illustrations by David Cousens © Franklin Watts 2011
Cover design by Jonathan Hair

Franklin Watts
338 Euston Road
London NW1 3BH

Franklin Watts Australia
Level 17/207 Kent Street
Sydney, NSW 2000

The author and illustrator have asserted their rights in
accordance with the Copyright, Designs and Patents Act, 1988.

All rights reserved. No part of this publication may be
reproduced, stored in a retrieval system, or transmitted
in any form or by any means, electronic, mechanical,
photocopy, recording or otherwise, without the prior
written permission of the copyright owner.

A CIP catalogue record for this book
is available from the British Library.

ISBN: 978 1 4451 0115 6

1 3 5 7 9 10 8 6 4 2

Printed in Great Britain

Franklin Watts is a division of Hachette Children's Books,
an Hachette UK company.
www.hachette.co.uk

USMC fighting knife
MkII and sheath

2 x water canteen

2 x Mk IIA1 fragmentation
grenade

AN/M14 thermite
grenade

USMC first-aid kit containing:
1 cotton OD case, 1 canvas Carlisle dressing belt
pouch, 1 insect repellent bottle, 2 bottles of iodine,
1 Carlisle small first-aid dressing, 1 first-aid packet
in olive-painted copper tin, 1 medium cotton wound
bandage, 1 sunburn paste tin, 2 cotton sterilised
bandages, 1 personal stitching/sewing kit.

It is February 1945, and the war in Europe is all but over. Yet the Americans are fighting a different war in the Pacific. The USA had been brought into World War II in 1941, after an unprovoked attack by Japanese forces at Pearl Harbor. Since then, US leaders put a plan in place to destroy the Japanese threat: to invade Japan, remove the Emperor from power and end the war. To do this they first needed to capture hundreds of small islands that stood between American forces and Japan.

The last of these islands is Iwo Jima.

Iwo Jima is a key target. It has a working airfield which, if captured, could be used to launch bombing raids on Japan. Yet the Japanese are not going to give up the island without a fight. They see it as sacred Japanese soil, and will fiercely defend it to keep it out of American hands.

The Americans' plan to capture Iwo Jima is simple. They will bombard the island from battleships at sea, and then send thousands of US Marines ashore to mop up. However, the plan has one flaw – the Japanese will know the attack is coming. They will have had weeks to prepare their defences, including miles of underground tunnels and concrete bunkers. The Japanese know they can't hold on to Iwo Jima for ever, but they intend to make the US Marines pay for the island in blood…

You are a US Marine in 28th Regiment, 5th Marine division. For the last few days you have been sitting on a battleship off the shore of Iwo Jima, watching as the volcanic island was bombarded by shells. You wondered if anything could survive such a pounding.

You are now on a motorised landing craft heading towards the black sandy beaches of Iwo Jima.

◊ *Go to section 1.*

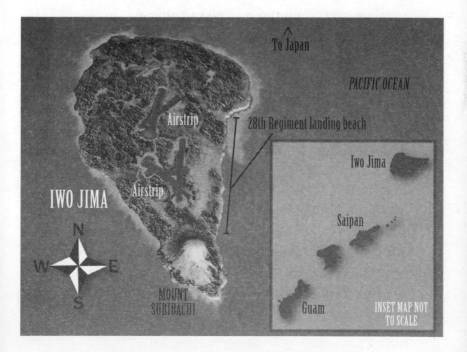

Morning – 19 February 1945

All you can see are the worried faces of your fellow Marines and the blue-grey sky that frames the sides of the landing craft. You squat uncomfortably on the metal floor, your pack and M1 Garand rifle weighing you down. The tracked boat bobs through the ocean, and the drone of the engine and the smell of diesel fuel all combine to make you feel very sick.

You lift yourself up and strain to see over the metal sides. You catch a glimpse of hundreds of other landing craft snaking through the water. You hear the boom of the huge battleship guns which continue to pound the tiny island ahead.

The boat powers onwards. As you edge closer to the beach, Japanese machine-gun bullets "ping" off the landing craft sides. You duck down, then, without warning a clatter of metal is followed by a thump as the ramp in front of you drops down...

Ahead of you is a wide beach, its black volcanic sand making it look like something from another planet. You are not the first to land, and hundreds of Marines are already scurrying about. You step forward, trying to ignore the dead bodies in the surf. The air is filled with the noise of battle, bullets whizz all about and dull explosions send spouts of hot black sand into the air.

The beach is flat, but it quickly rises into a steep

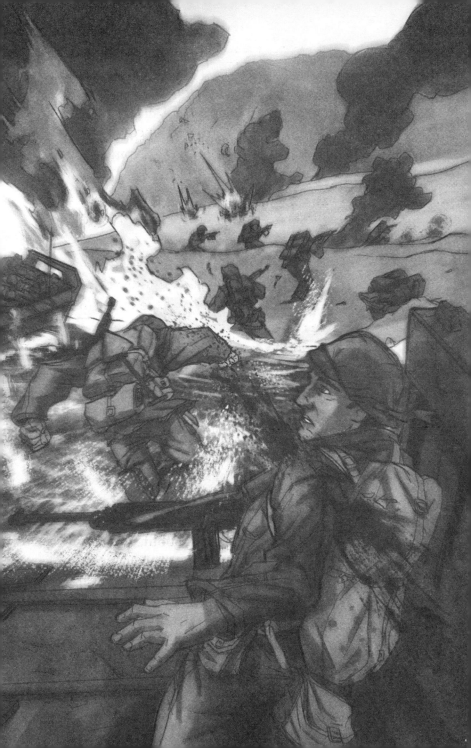

wall of sand. With little option you stagger into the surf, the soft sand slipping away underneath your boots. Water soaks through your socks. Marines around you shout and push, urging each other onwards. You stumble again. Suddenly a Marine to your right screams and spins into the water as he is hit. Bullets rip through the air all around you.

◊ *To run to the safety of the sand dune ahead of you, go to 35.*

◊ *To do as you have been trained, and begin to dig in to create a hole where you can take cover, go to 82.*

---

2 *Afternoon – 19 February 1945*

All of your training has told you not to trust the Japanese, and you know that you need to make sure that the pillbox is empty. However, to get inside you will have to move the charred body. You turn to Tex and tell him to cover you. As you get near the blocked doorway, you peer into the gloom. You can't see anything. You need to go inside to be sure it's clear.

You use the butt of your M1 Garand to lever the body away from the entrance.

You can't see them, but under the body are two grenades – placed in such a way so they will explode when the body is moved; it's a booby trap.

The grenades explode, launching you backwards and peppering your body with hundreds of shards of molten metal. You are dead before you hit the ground.

◊ *You've been killed by a Japanese booby trap. Go to 84 to discover your fate.*

Morning – 19 February 1945

3

An attack across open ground would be suicide, so you have little choice but to wait. The Marines around you open fire on the pillbox, but they are having little effect. You focus on the black slit and fire off a few shots, but stop when you realise you are just wasting ammunition. The machine gun continues to splutter bullets in your direction.

Suddenly, a huge explosion erupts to the right of the pillbox; orange flame licks out in all directions. You are confused, but the machine gun stops firing for a moment. Then, as the sand and smoke clears, it starts up again.

To your left you can hear a strange noise. Over the snap of rifle fire and distant explosions of battle, you can make out the rumble of an engine and a loud metallic squeak. Emerging from behind a fold in the ground is a Sherman tank!

A cheer ripples through the Marines as the tank takes up position and thunders another shell at the pillbox. Yet, once again the shot flies wide, causing a flash of fire and eruption of sand, but failing to silence the machine gun.

You realise that the tank is too close, and the tank crew can't target the pillbox accurately. In training, you were taught to direct tank fire using the external phone link on the back of the tank.

◊ *If you wish to dodge between the rocks and direct the tank's fire, go to 97.*

◊ *If you wish to stay where you are and let a Marine closer to the tank direct the fire, go to 32.*

Morning – 19 February 1945

4

You check the explosives one more time, hold the trigger in your left hand and place the satchel in your right. After the machine gun has spluttered a short burst, you jump to your feet.

The next few seconds happen in a blur. As you stand up you catch your first glimpse of the enemy. Huddled in the pillbox are two teenage Japanese soldiers.

You stuff the satchel though the narrow slot – it's just like delivering a letter – and then dive to the left of the pillbox. As you hit the sand you let the thin wire unravel and then twist the trigger.

A boom sends sand, smoke and chunks of concrete in all directions. For a moment your ears ring and you are left confused, but you quickly recover. With a smile on your face you run back to the crater.

As you slump back into the safety of the hole

in the sand you see that the Sergeant is gone. The three Marines left in the crater slap you on the back. You are just feeling smug when the machine gun begins firing again! The Japanese must have retaken the wrecked pillbox.

You glance over the lip of crater when a hand pulls you down. A young Marine is right next to you. The noise from the MG is so loud you can't hear him speak. Instead he nods in the direction of the bottom of the crater. You turn to see a flame-thrower lying in the black sand.

◊ *If you wish to put on the flame-thrower and clear out the pillbox, go to 59.*

◊ *If you think it is time someone else risked their life, go to 17.*

---

5 *Morning – 19 February 1945*

You push yourself to your feet and snatch a small white slip of paper from the Sergeant. He looks surprised, but without a word he turns away from you and strides along the line of Marines.

You duck down and jog back the way you came, skirting the burned-out pillbox, heading towards the beach. Once on the beach you try to navigate the hell that is unfolding in front of your eyes. Machine-gun fire rakes the landing area; burning vehicles send plumes of black smoke into the air; enemy mortar shells occasionally thud into the beach, spraying fire and sand. After about thirty minutes of picking your way along the beach, you see a small group of Marines. You find the highest ranking officer and pass him the paper. He reads it, thanks you and sets about his business.

Once again you thread your way through the death and destruction on the beach. You climb over the dune but you can't find the burned-out pillbox. You head inland anyway. You pause for a moment and scan the area ahead. You are lost. It is difficult to see far since the sand rises and falls. Small black volcanic rocks are scattered all about. Without warning, machine-gun fire spurts sand up at your feet. You dive behind the nearest rock. The MG stops and you peer around to see a pillbox just a few metres ahead. The MG is turned in your direction. Your only option is to run back the way you have come.

◊ *To say a prayer before running, go to 30.*
◊ *To just start running because you feel God has abandoned Iwo Jima, go to 86.*

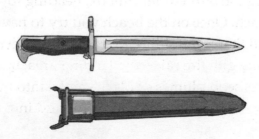

6

You smile, remove your bayonet from its sheath and hand it to Mike. He glows like a school boy and attaches it to the end of his M1 rifle.

With just a few minutes to go before the attack, a loud rumble can be heard in the sky. You look out to sea and spot a mass of planes coming in your direction. As they near your position they dip low and, one at a time, fire salvos of deadly rockets. These scream in low over your crater and slam into the Japanese defences. The planes come wave after wave, and with each crash of rockets you sink a little deeper into the sand, your hand pulled up to protect your face.

As the last plane turns away and a relative quiet returns to the battlefield, you know it is time to attack.

◊ *Go to 54.*

7 *Night – 19 February 1945*

You don't recognise "Studebaker" and immediately loose off a couple of shots into the darkness. You wait a moment and are sure you can hear a soft moan. You wait a few minutes more before relaxing slightly.

Night returns. You are cold and your fingers are numb. With each flare you strain in the artificial light to see if you can spot movement. Time passes and the night drags by. You feel hungry and alone. You have no idea of the time and feel yourself drifting into sleep, when you are sure you hear the sound of small pebbles falling between rocks.

You shout out "Ford". There is no response.

◊ *If you wish to shoot towards the sound, go to 52.*
◊ *If you wish to wait and be certain, go to 40.*

---

8 *Afternoon – 20 February 1945*

The thick mass of bushes seems the most likely hiding place for the sniper. You ease yourself to the edge of the crater and remain on your stomach, focusing your attention on the bushes. You peer down the sights of your rifle and wait.

You never see the Japanese sniper as he creeps from his hiding place in the cave. He aims at your head, and with a single shot, shoots you dead.

◊ *A Japanese sniper's bullet has ended your battle. Go to 84 to discover your fate.*

Even before your hand reaches the cold metal of your rifle, you know it is the wrong choice. The Japanese officer is running at full speed and as you lean down he is upon you. You move to try to block his blow, but he is a skilled swordsman. He lets the blade swing low and then slices sharply across your stomach.

You fall backwards into the dirt – the Japanese officer has gone.

You are left clutching yourself, trying to stop your insides spilling out. You call out into the dark for your mother. It takes about an hour for you to die.

◊ *Your battle has ended with your agonising death. Go to 84 to discover your fate.*

10 *Night – 20 February 1945*

You don't wish to tempt fate and seeing a mortar explode in your old shell hole is enough to make you seek out a new home. You creep about in the darkness for a few minutes, the odd bullet cracking off in the darkness, until you finally discover a small, but deep, crater. You slip into the hole, closely followed by Tex and Mike.

This night is as intense as the previous one – with the constant threat of attack, white flares and sporadic mortar fire – meaning you get very little sleep. At one point, deep into the night, you hear a loud explosion from the direction of the beach, and for a few minutes afterwards a dull orange glow can be seen in the night sky. Later still, your sleep is once again washed away by bright white circles of light that crisscross the mountainside. These are searchlights from the battleships anchored a few miles off the island. The lights are followed by a period of heavy bombardment, and as you lie in the crater, you can feel the ground shake and rumble as the US shells pound into the side of the mountain.

When daylight finally arrives next morning, you suspect you have had no more than an hour's broken sleep.

◊ *Go to 66.*

11 *Morning – 19 February 1945*

You have been trained to find cover when you are exposed, and if there is no cover, then dig a hole. So that is what you do – you start to dig with your bayonet and your hands. The sand is hot and stinks of rotten eggs. As you dig, the sand quickly slips back into your hole. You create a shallow hole, which you crawl into and wait for orders.

Minutes pass, and no orders come. You fumble in your pack, pull out a chocolate bar and stuff a piece into your mouth. Someone nearby shouts "incoming", and a thud some distance to your left is followed by an explosion and a shower of sand. A second explosion is closer, while a third shell lands just a metre from your hole. You press into the ground, black sand splattering onto your body and half burying you. Another three explosions keep you cowering in the sand.

Then it stops. You look about to see the corpsman attending wounded Marines. Screams of pain fill the air. You stay in your hole.

◊ *Go to 60.*

12 *Night – 19 February 1945*

The Japanese officer is almost on you. You squat into a crouching position, M1 Garand – bayonet fixed – across your body with the blade pointing towards the enemy's throat.

Your training comes flooding back and you remember your instructor's word "fight like a boxer". You move your feet, pacing to the right. The officer's sword is too low and his run is uncontrolled. You knock away his blade with the butt of your rifle and sidestep as he comes past. Swinging around, you thrust your bayonet into the hollow of his back. He stumbles and falls. You quickly deal out two swift stabs to his back. It takes a while longer for your heart to stop racing. You reposition yourself in the rocks, just a few metres from the dead soldier.

The remainder of the night passes under the same eerie atmosphere. The occasional flares bathe you in white light and the darkness brings shouts of "Ford" and "Chrysler", together with the odd burst of gunfire.

You are happy to see the Sun finally rise above the horizon.

◊ *Go to 96.*

Afternoon – 19 February 1945

You have completely lost your original unit, but after a quick word with a Sergeant, you are told to tag along until you find your commander. You set out across the sand in a zigzag line. To your left and right are Marines you have only just met. The one on the right is a tall, well-built man with a face from a cowboy film. He speaks in a slow southern drawl and carries the name Tex. The man to the left is smaller – an Italian with black hair, called Mike.

You advance through the sand dunes before crossing into an area of black, rocky soil, with bushes and twisted trees sprouting from between the boulders. As the day wears on, you stumble across a maze of trenches. These have been dug by the Japanese defenders and crisscross in the general direction of your advance. Dead bodies – both American and Japanese – show that a battle has recently raged here.

You are instructed to move into the trenches,

which are about waist high, and as you move you feel yourself crouching in order to make the most of the cover. You tread your way down the trenches, with Tex in front by a few paces and Mike covering your rear.

As you advance, a squat pillbox looms up ahead. The trench runs parallel to the pillbox and you will need to pass right in front of the black slit. Tex signals for you to stop and as you examine the pillbox you see that the sides of the structure are blackened by fire, and there is no sign of movement inside.

◊ *If you wish to investigate the pillbox, go to 44.*
◊ *If you wish to ignore the pillbox, go to 78.*

14 *Morning – 21 February 1945*

Tex and Mike want to keep moving, but you signal them to stop for a moment. Pulling yourself to the lip of the crater you look out at the destruction ahead. Hundreds of Marines lie dead or dying in the black sand, while bullets fizz about and explosions flash to your left and right.

As you look on, a bullet from an unseen Japanese gunman passes cleanly through your chest and you slump back into the crater. It takes a few moments before Tex and Mike realise that they have lost their new friend.

◊ *A Japanese sniper's bullet has ended your battle.*
   Go to 84 to discover your fate.

---

15 *Morning – 19 February 1945*

You take a deep breath, check the BAR's safety catch is off, and run. Your target is a hole that has been blasted in the sand by a shell, probably from one of your battleships anchored off the coast.

The first few metres go well, your feet coping with the shifting sand, your eyes glued to the ground, watching for obstacles that could trip you. Then the Japanese machine gun opens up once again. You look up to see orange flames spitting from the pillbox slot. You zigzag as you run, sand spurting up at your feet from bullets, before launching yourself into the hole.

For a moment you lie still as the MG's bullets buzz over your head. Then the gun falls silent. You ease the muzzle of the BAR over the lip of the shell hole and send a few rounds towards the pillbox. Suddenly four Marines jump down into the sand next to you – the Sergeant and three other Marines, none of whom you recognise.

The Sergeant looks at you. A huge unlit Cuban cigar is clamped firmly between his teeth.

"Still feeling unlucky?" he asks, his voice muffled by the cigar. Then, without waiting for your reply, he drops a brown satchel of explosives into your lap. "You've got this far, Marine, you might as well give the Japs a real US of A hello."

◊ *If you wish to do as the Sergeant orders and try to blow up the pillbox, go to 65.*

◊ *If you think you have risked your life enough for this man, go to 24.*

16 *Morning – 21 February 1945*

Without a further thought you slump forward and roll onto the grenade. You can feel the hard, round shape under your stomach as you lie still. You glance up to see Tex. You scream for him to run. The next second the grenade explodes. Your body absorbs the lethal blast, and though you are blown in half, Tex is left unharmed.

◊ *Your heroic sacrifice has saved your friends, but you have paid the ultimate price. Now go to 84.*

---

17 *Morning – 19 February 1945*

You look at the young Marine and shake your head. He has bright blue eyes, and can't be more than 18 years old. He understands what you are saying and a thin smile forms on his lips.

You watch as he scrambles to the base of the crater and lifts the heavy flame-thrower onto his back. It consists of a metal backpack, which contains the fuel, along with a gun-like hose, from which the flames will leap. He struggles to get the flame-thrower into a comfortable position on his back, but soon he is ready.

"Give me some covering fire," he says as he scrambles past you to the lip of the crater.

You poke your head over the edge of the hole and start letting off small bursts from your BAR. The two other Marines soon join you. Suddenly your guns jams and no matter how many times you try, you can't get the gun to work. You throw the useless lump of metal away and retrieve your M1 rifle. After a few minutes the Japanese machine gun stops firing.

You scan to your left and see the young Marine moving forward. As he gets close to the pillbox he stands up and a tongue of fire leaps from the flame-thrower. He directs the jet into the silt of the pillbox. The young Marine stands for a couple of seconds; flames blasting out of the slit and black smoke rising quickly into the sky. Eventually, he stops firing, ducks down and jogs back to your crater.

◊ *Go to 42.*

18 *Afternoon – 21 February 1945*

You are about to suggest to Mike that you should attack, when he leans in close. "Wait," he says, pointing over your shoulder.

You look over where two Marines are strapping on flame-throwers. You exchange a smile with Mike, and start firing at the pillbox.

From your concealed position amongst the rocks you are able to fire into the black slit. At first the machine gun returns fire, then for a moment it falls silent. The rest of your unit have now caught up and they also starting firing on the pillbox.

The two Marines with flame-throwers seize the moment and stagger forward from their cover, under the weight of the heavy weapons. They move up over the rough ground, until both flame-throwers spit into life. The two spurts of flame lick into the pillbox. Over the roar of the fire you can hear the screams of the men inside. After about ten seconds the flames subside. The battlefield suddenly falls quiet.

The eerie silence is broken by the noise of a tank engine. A Sherman tank rolls up, its progress slow and cautious.

◊ *To push ahead of the tank and continue the attack past the pillbox, go to 26.*

◊ *To let the tank move ahead and advance behind it, go to 48.*

19 *Morning – 21 February 1945*

You dodge round the crater and continue to race forward blindly. Tex and Mike push past you. They weave to the left to avoid an obstacle. You are slow to react, and you nearly stumble and fall on a headless corpse lying in the dirt.

You recover your footing and look up to see a small pillbox just up ahead. It is buried in the sand with just the black slit showing. Sand has been stacked up on either side, leaving an easy route to the flat roof. As you watch you see Mike slip and fall in the black sand. Tex manages to clamber up on to the roof of the pillbox.

◊ *If you wish to dive for cover next to Mike, go to 23.*
◊ *If you wish to join Tex on the roof of the pillbox, go to 71.*

20 *Morning – 20 February 1945*

The gunfire and noise of battle is deafening and you have to shout to make yourself heard. In a scream you explain to Tex and Mike that you are going to go back to the tank. They nod, relieved that they will not have to attack the crater. Without a further word you are up and running.

The path back to the tank is strewn with jagged black rocks and the sand beneath your feet slips and slides as you run. Once again you zigzag to avoid enemy gunfire. With each step you await the thump of a bullet, but it never comes. Suddenly the tank looms large in front of you, and you slide in behind the machine.

You scramble to find the metal box that contains the phone. You open the small metal flap and see

that the phone handset has been ripped from the wire. Without thinking, you duck back out from behind the tank up to the front. Using the butt of your rifle you bang on the side of the tank and then point in the direction of the crater.

At first nothing happens and you stand exposed, bullets pinging off the tank. Then the turret swings in the direction of the crater. You spring to the rear of the tank and throw yourself to the ground.

The first two shells miss the crater, exploding behind it. The third is a direct hit and even from where you lie you can see bodies being thrown into the air. You spring back to your feet, salute in the direction of the tank, and race back to where Tex and Mike are sheltering. It is not long before shouts to push forward echo across the battlefield.

◊ *Go to 67.*

Morning – 21 February 1945

You lift your M1 Garand rifle to your shoulder
and fire off a couple of shots. The enemy are not
far away, but they are moving quickly and making
the most of the cover. Slowly you realise that there
are lots of Japanese helmets bobbing about in
the trenches and you pick shots at them, without
knowing if you are hitting any. Marines behind
you are scuttling down the trenches with brown
wooden boxes of grenades in their arms.

You turn back to the battle and are just about to
let off another shot when you feel a thump in the
chest. You are thrown backwards and lose grip of
your rifle. Lying on your back in the trench you try
to lift yourself, but you can't find the strength. You
look down at your chest where your uniform has
been replaced by a mass of red blood and tissue.
The realisation that your wounds are fatal sends
you into shock and you soon black out, never to
awake.

◊ *The Battle of Iwo Jima is over for you. Go to 84 to
discover your fate.*

Night – 19 February 1945

You wait, straining to hear in the darkness. Suddenly a flare fizzes into life high above your head, and the area in front of your position is flooded with white light. You are shocked to see a Japanese soldier standing about ten metres from your position. He looks in your direction and a brief smile flashes onto his moustached face. Before you can react he throws a grenade that loops high into the air and lands at your feet.

You react quickly, throwing yourself backwards, but you are still too slow. The blast pushes the air from your lungs and thrusts you onto the ground. Your body is flooded with fire, heat and shrapnel.

When you come to, it is morning. You are lying on the beach on a stretcher. You look to your right and left to see other wounded soldiers, also on stretchers. You look down to see that both of your legs have been heavily bandaged. A corpsman sees you are awake and moves next to you.

"You are one lucky boy," he says with a smile. "Looks like you will be on the next boat home."

You once again look down at your smashed legs and wonder if you will ever walk again.

◊ *The Battle of Iwo Jima is over for you. Though your wound is serious enough for a ticket home, you will survive this battle… Go back to 1 to try again.*

You glance up at Tex and then dive down next to Mike. You push yourself down hard as bullets whistle just above you. After a few seconds you lift your head to see Tex firing erratically from the roof of the pillbox. Then he suddenly stops firing and kicks what looks like a stone from in front of him. You watch as the stone arcs through the air coming directly towards where you and Mike are lying. Too late you realise it is not a stone, but a grenade! The grenade explodes while still in the air, showering you and Mike with red-hot metal.

At first you think you have survived the blast, but then you see the red stream of blood spurting from a hole in your neck. You try to scream but you can't. You bring your hand up to the gooey mess that was once your throat. You can do nothing but lie in the black sand as your lifeblood pumps away, listening to Mike scream for a corpsman.

◊ *Though you've fought bravely, you have run out of luck. Go to 84 to discover your fate.*

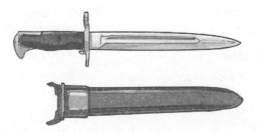

Morning – 19 February 1945

You have not had the best morning, and this rude man is just too much for you. You slam your fist into the sand in anger and grab the satchel by the handle. You hold it out to the Sergeant and tell him to send someone else. Bullets continue to whizz just centimetres above your head.

For a moment the Sergeant sits motionless, his huge unlit cigar hanging loosely in his mouth. He looks at your face, then at the satchel, then back to your face.

The seconds tick by as you both sit in silence. The roar of battle is deafening, but it seems to have slipped into the background.

Finally the Sergeant acts. He ignores your outstretched hand, and instead flips open the leather cover of his holster and brings out a silver Colt .45. You notice how beautiful the weapon is, with its white mother-of-pearl hand grip.

"Now, soldier," says the Sergeant, cocking the weapon's hammer and thrusting the muzzle in your face. "You either blow up that Jap pillbox or I blow up your head. Your choice."

◊ *The Sergeant gives you no option but to attack the pillbox. Go to 65.*

You tell Tex and Mike to go on. You explain that you will help the wounded Marine and then come back to find them.

You crouch down and pull the Marine to his feet – he winces in pain. You sling your rifle onto your shoulder and place one arm around the Marine before you start the slow trudge back along the trenches.

The Sun is high and the strain of supporting the Marine is hard work. The man has not spoken for over thirty minutes. The going is tough and you have not moved far when you need to stop for a drink. You lower the Marine to the ground and remove your canteen from your pack. You stand up fully to help relax your muscles.

The first shot passes through your hand and the water bottle as you bring it to your lips. The second hits you in the chest. You slump to the ground and black out.

When you come to, the blind Marine is helplessly fumbling a dirty bandage onto the gaping hole in your chest. You try to speak, but death silences you.

◊ *You let down your guard and paid the ultimate price. Go to 84 to discover your fate.*

26 *Afternoon – 21 February 1945*

You are keen to push on. You run forward, picking your way through the rocks and black sand, glancing up at the imposing mountain that rises high above you. You reach the burned-out pillbox and take cover behind a collapsed wall. From here you can see that the noise from the Sherman seems to have awoken the Japanese defenders, and more and more incoming fire is directed at the tank. Ducked down behind the tank is a growing line of Marines, taking shelter behind its metal bulk.

You look over your shoulder, but see no sign of Mike. The ground around you is littered with rocks and you lift yourself to your feet to try to locate your comrade. Within seconds of standing a bullet from a Japanese sniper rifle thuds into your body. It impacts just below your cheekbone, smashing teeth and bone. For a moment you stand upright, your finger poking in the hole in your face. Then you collapse into the dirt.

◊ *A Japanese sniper's bullet has ended your battle.*
Go to 84 to discover your fate.

---

27 *Afternoon – 20 February 1945*

You edge yourself to the lip of the crater, and lying on your stomach you aim at the group of rocks a few hundred metres ahead. They seem like the ideal hiding place for a sniper.

You target the rocks with your rifle, finger poised on the trigger. When the movement comes it is not in the rocks but further back, at the cave entrance. Out of the corner of your eye you see a shape pop into view. You swing your rifle and squeeze the trigger, letting off a wild shot.

As you try to locate the sniper again, you see a flash and feel a thump on your right shoulder. You let out a scream and roll into the safety of the crater. Looking down you see a huge hole at the top of your arm. You try to stay awake, but the pain is unbearable.

"Hang on!" Tex screams, as blackness overcomes you. He fumbles a white bandage onto the wound, but it is deep, and even with your friend's best efforts, you are dead before the corpsmen arrive in your small shell hole.

◊ *A Japanese sniper's bullet has ended your battle. Go to 84 to discover your fate.*

Afternoon – 21 February 1945
You trudge back along the route you have just
taken and find a group of Marines at the trench
complex. You head for the pillbox where you last
saw Tex. You climb onto the roof, but you can't see
any sign of your fellow Marine's body.

The fighting in this area has stopped, and
while you can hear distant sounds of battle, it
is relatively quiet. As you walk away from the
pillbox, you hear a faint cry. It is coming from a
patch of black sand to your left. You move towards
the sound until you locate its source.

You are surprised to see that the noise is coming
from a Japanese soldier. All that you can see are
his round face and helmet. The rest of his body is
covered in sand. You can only guess that he has
been buried by a shell blast.

A smile flashes on his pale face as you crouch
down next to him. He looks you in the eye and,
with great effort, pulls his arm free from the sand.
You look around but can't see any other men. In
fact, all you can see is sand and black rocks.

Looking back at the Japanese solider you see
he has moved his fingers in front of his face and is
making a V sign, indicating he wants a cigarette.

◊ *If you wish to give the Japanese soldier a cigarette,*
  go to 37.
◊ *If you wish to ignore the enemy soldier, go to 69.*

29 Night – 20 February 1945

You aim your rifle into the gloom and squeeze the trigger. The crack of the rifle shot echoes out. Somewhere behind you Tex and Mike are digging out the crater.

Suddenly a shape looms up – it's a Japanese soldier! He is running at you, the sharp point of his bayonet aimed towards your body. He is only about five metres away. You lift your rifle, take steady aim and squeeze the trigger. Nothing happens! Your rifle has jammed! You fumble with the bolt, but the enemy soldier is upon you. With a quick thrust he buries his bayonet into your shoulder. Pain streaks through you – again and again he thrusts. A crack of a rifle rings out and the Japanese soldier is gone. You slump back into the crater. The last things you see before you die are the horrified faces of Tex and Mike.

◊ *Your dirty rifle has cost you your life. Go to 84 to discover your fate.*

30 Morning – 19 February 1945

You close your eyes and silently mouth the words to the Lord's Prayer. You then glance around the small black rock, count to three and run.

The first couple of steps are made before the Japanese can react. Your boots slip and slide in the shifting black sand, and you struggle to pick up any real speed. You are heading back the way you have come, up and over a small hump in the sand; if you can make it to the other side the Japanese soldiers in the pillbox will not be able to see you.

Suddenly the rattle of the machine gun brings bursts of sand at your feet, and the whistle of lethal bullets in the air around your ears. You first zig to the right, and then zag to the left – all the time pumping your legs.

With a final superhuman effort, you leap over the lip of the sand and roll into the safety behind. The MG falls silent.

You wait for a couple of minutes to regain your breath. You have no idea which way to go so you crouch down and set off to your right. After a few minutes you see the shapes of some Marines lying in a bomb crater. You jog up to their position and jump into the hole.

◊   *Go to 60.*

Morning – 22 February 1945

You have trained as a Marine to fight, not carry boxes, and you choose to remain in the reserves. The clouds in the sky suggest the rain will last all day. You pick your way through the rocks, feeling relaxed. It is still not totally safe, but most of the enemy have been pushed away from the beach area, so you can walk without worrying about stumbling onto a machine gun position.

You find Mike, who has found a shell hole and is busy digging out the dark sand. You join him and together you make the hole bigger. Mike then jumps out and is gone for about an hour. When he returns he is carrying a green poncho – like the one you are both wearing – four wooden poles and two tins.

He sets about opening the tins. The first contains turkey, the second peaches in syrup. Together you sit in the rain and eat the best meal of your life.

As the Sun sets you find yourself in a more comfortable position than the previous night. Mike has fastened a green poncho to four sticks and created a homely, and more importantly, dry tented area. This rain has eased and you look forward to some sleep.

◊ *Go to 46.*

Morning – 19 February 1945
You never have liked stinking, noisy tanks and decide to let some other chump direct the fire. You settle down in the sand with your rifle at the ready.

The next shell that comes from the tank is too far to the left, and though the explosion is impressive, the machine gun starts firing again just moments after the impact. A few minutes pass and you begin to wonder if the tank has given up. A thundering boom from the tank answers you, and you watch as the shell scores a direct hit on the front of the pillbox. A muffled explosion flings sand and concrete into the air. When the smoke clears, all that is left of the pillbox is a mound of ripped sandbags and a couple of broken walls.

A ripple of claps and cheers erupts as the Marine directing the action jogs back to his position in the line. You watch him as he moves, his face seems familiar, but you can't quite place it.

The Sun is now high in the sky and you wait in silence for the next orders.

◊ *Go to 13.*

Morning – 21 February 1945
You look at Mike and shake your head. You explain that you need your bayonet and he nods. You know you have made the right choice, but you can't help feeling sorry for the Italian.

With just a few minutes to go before the attack, you hear a loud rumble in the sky. You look out to sea and spot a mass of planes coming in your direction. As they near your position they dip low and one at a time release salvos of deadly rockets. These scream in over your crater and slam into the Japanese defences. The planes come in wave after wave, and with each crash of rockets you sink a little deeper into the sand, your hand pulled up to protect your face.

As the last plane turns away and a relative quiet returns to the battlefield, you know it is time to attack.

◊ *Go to 54.*

---

34 *Morning – 21 February 1945*
The trench system is complex and twists away ahead of you. The Japanese are using the trenches to move forward, but they have to slow down at the places where the trenches bend, or when they come under fire from Marines. You decide to focus on these areas.

You unclip two grenades from your belt, pull the pin on the first and toss it high towards the enemy, followed closely by the second grenade. You are pleased when both grenades explode right on target.

A burly Marine staggers up behind you. He is bent over, with sweat streaming down his red cheeks. He is carrying a wooden box. He stops just in front of you and without speaking places the box on the ground and pulls open the lid. The box is full of grenades!

You bend down, pick up a grenade, whip out the pin and hurl the metal bomb towards the Japanese in the trenches. It explodes; you duck down, grab another and throw again. More Marines join you, delving into the box like it's full of Christmas presents. Grenade after grenade arcs high into the air and it is not long before your arm is sore and the fingers on your left hand are red from pulling out metal grenade pins.

As the grenades start to run out, you realise that you can't see any enemy soldiers. You can see dead bodies and the occasional bobbing helmet, but they are no longer trying to counter-attack. A smile forms on your face but only lasts for a moment. Suddenly a scream of "incoming" is followed by the thud and boom of mortar shells. You duck down into the trench as shell after shell explodes around you, showering you with dirt and sand.

◊ *Go to 58.*

Morning – 19 February 1945

You see a stream of Marines sprinting from the water to the safety of the sand dune just a few paces ahead. You decide this is your best chance of surviving the next few minutes.

Putting your head down, you start running. At first your heavy pack, and the shifting sand and water, slow your pace. You can see hundreds of Marines all around you; some are floating dead in the surf. Others are badly wounded as Japanese shells explode on the beach, throwing sand and men into the air.

However, once you are out of the water you make quick progress. You whisper a quick prayer under your breath as you run. Finally, with an almighty effort, you hurl yourself into the side of the dune and bury your face into the sand. Bullets whizz over your head, filling the air.

When you finally lift your head you can see that you are surrounded by about twenty Marines huddled in the sand, none of whom you recognise. The Marine immediately to your right is trying to dig a hole into the side of the dune, whilst the other Marines just lie still.

◊ *If you wish to dig in like the Marine to your right, go to 56.*

◊ *If you wish to wait in the sand, go to 94.*

You nod to Tex. He smiles, checks his rifle, winks at Mike and they run. You are close behind as the Japanese open fire.

It is about ten metres from the tank to the crater. The ground rises up towards the base of Mount Suribachi; it is steep and sandy, with rocks and bushes everywhere. Shell holes and craters are dotted about, providing cover for US Marines and Japanese soldiers. It is impossible to see where the Japanese are hiding, but from the amount of enemy gunfire, you know they are close.

You zigzag as you run, before finally diving into the safety of the hole. Mike and Tex are already lying in the crater, panting heavily. As you roll next to them, you look at each other and laugh.

Just then, a Marine crashes down next to you. He is young, his face covered with dirt and blood. He explains that you need to attack a crater just ahead. You creep forward and peek over the rim. The ground is littered with black rocks and wiry bushes, but you can see the crater. Occasionally popping into view you can see the distinctive shape of about four or five Japanese helmets.

◊ *If you wish to attack the crater with Tex and Mike, go to 74.*

◊ *If you wish to brave the enemy gunfire and direct the tank to fire a few shells into the crater, go to 20.*

Afternoon – 21 February 1945

You rummage in your backpack and produce a battered packet of cigarettes. You carefully pull one out and light it before handing it to the Japanese soldier. He takes the cigarette, smiles and takes a long puff. He then offers you the cigarette – you shake your head and hold up your hand to show he should keep it.

"Thank you," he says. You are shocked that he can speak English.

You ask him where he learned English. He shrugs and says that he lived in the USA for five years. He went to Columbia University in New York. He says he still has many American friends and hopes to visit them once the war is over.

You continue talking until a corpsman and a group of five Marines arrive. You say goodbye to the trapped solider. It is now getting dark.

◊ *Go to 81.*

38 *Morning – 23 February 1945*

You join two other Marines to make a group of four. They both nod in recognition as you move closer.

It is not long before you set off up the mountain. The first group of four Marines is about fifty metres in front of you, and they quickly snake out along the path. You pick your way up the path, which rises steeply and twists around the side of the mountain. As the path rises the landscape changes. The mountain is strewn with large rocks and twisted bushes. Yet the thing that unsettles you is the mountainside, with its small ravines, slits and caves providing numerous hiding places for enemy soldiers.

You nervously plod onwards for about fifteen minutes, when the lead Marine suddenly thrusts his hand in the air and drops to one knee. The Marine points about ten metres ahead and to the left, his finger poking towards the dark entrance of a cave.

"Jap, I think…" he whispers hoarsely.

◊ *If you wish to investigate the cave, go to 68.*
◊ *If you wish to ignore the cave and keep moving, go to 100.*

Morning – 23 February 1945

Your orders were to see if the mountain was clear
of Japanese soldiers, and you have done this. You
indicate to the other group that you are going to
head down and they wave in acknowledgment.

The trek back down is much like the climb up,
slow and careful. Now though you can look out
across Iwo Jima. Only from this height do you get
a sense of how small the island really is. You can
see smoke rising further inland, especially around
the airstrip and at the opposite tip of the island.

A savage, ear-pounding explosion knocks you
off your feet and down the track. You let out an
involuntary cry as the blast sweeps over you and
you land flat on your back. Your left leg feels like
it is on fire and you look down to see that your
trouser leg and a large area of skin and flesh
have been torn away. The wound is ugly. The leg
muscle has been sliced open and exposed. Without
thinking you reach down and try to join flesh,
only succeeding in sending a fresh wave of pain
through your body.

◊ *The Battle of Iwo Jima is over for you. Though
your wound is serious enough for a ticket home,
you will survive this battle… Now go to 70 to
discover your fate.*

You wait, straining to hear in the darkness. Suddenly a flare fizzes into life high above your head and the area in front of your position is flooded with white light. You are shocked to see a Japanese soldier standing about ten metres in front of you. He looks in your direction and a brief smile flashes onto his moustached face. Before you can react he throws a grenade that loops high into the air and lands at your feet.

You move quickly, throwing yourself backwards, but you are still too slow. The blast pushes the air from your lungs and hot metal shreds your flesh. Your body is flooded by fire, heat, sand and shrapnel. It is actually the shockwave from the grenade that kills you, with the energy from the explosion ripping through your body and turning your internal organs to mush. As the flare dies, your lifeless body disappears into the darkness.

◊ *You failed to act quickly when you most needed to, and have paid the ultimate price. Now go to 84.*

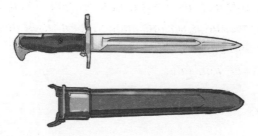

41 *Afternoon – 23 February 1945*

Together with the other group you spread out
to form a secure perimeter around the summit
of Suribachi. The Sun is high in the sky and
you sit motionless, watching the island below.
After about an hour you see another group of
Marines threading their way up the mountainside.
Eventually they reach the summit. One of the
Marines then pulls out an American flag from
inside his jacket. He lets it unfurl and for a moment
the Stars and Stripes flutter in the strong breeze.
The Marines search around until one finds a long
metal pole. They attach the flag to the pole and
hoist it high into the air where it is clearly visible
to all on the island.

You look down onto Iwo Jima; you are sure
that for a moment the fighting stops. For a brief
second it almost feels like a victory, and you're
certain that now the Battle of Iwo Jima will turn
in your favour. But you are unsure what the battle
will bring for you...

◊ *Now to go 70 to discover your fate.*

Morning – 19 February 1945

With the pillbox silent, the Marines around you prepare to move forward. You take a second to scan your surroundings. Ahead of you is an expanse of flat, black sand pitted by shell craters. To your left a huge mountain dominates the landscape – Mount Suribachi.

You hear an order to move forward, and you join the rest of the Marines around you as they rise to their feet and set out across the hot, black sand.

Overhead you hear the buzz of an engine and soon see the unmistakable shape of a Corsair. As you watch, the plane swoops low over the beaches, whilst to your left a "thud-thud" sound signals the Japanese anti-aircraft guns are following the plane's flight. Suddenly, the Corsair rocks in the air, black smoke trailing from its forward-mounted engine. The plane wobbles and then dips violently to the right. The pilot fights to keep control. The plane pitches towards the ground, and to your horror you watch it crash into the side of a US half-track that has made its way from the beach.

You plod on as if nothing has happened, making your way past the burned-out pillbox and onto the sand behind. Suddenly the stuttering of machine-gun fire sends everyone scrambling. You lie motionless, scanning for the source.

As you lift up from the sand, a familiar face

catches your attention. It is the Sergeant. He
sees you and smiles, his unlit cigar still clamped
between his teeth.

"Just the Marine," he snarls. "The units up
ahead have lost contact with the artillery on the
beach. We need a volunteer to go back and give the
co-ordinates of the next barrage."

◊ *If you wish to volunteer for the task, go to 5.*
◊ *If you feel you have already volunteered for enough,*
   go to 73.

Night – 20 February 1945   **43**
You lift yourself from your shallow hole and
scurry about in the near darkness looking for
better cover. It takes you about ten minutes to
find a deeper hole that offers more protection.
It takes another ten minutes to go back to tell
your comrades and then take position in the
new shell hole.

You are just settling in when you see three
Marines weaving their way past you, talking
loudly to avoid being shot by other Marines.
It is completely dark when they finally return,
heaving coils of barbed wire.

A shout of "incoming" sends you scrabbling
to the base of your crater. Tex, Mike and you
crouch down as mortar shells explode all around.
At one point you ease up your head and look

about. You are sure that the shells are coming down around the shallow hole you have recently moved away from.

Once you are sure the mortars have stopped you crawl to the lip of the crater and look out into the night's gloom. A few metres ahead you spot someone moving about. You call out "Ford" and wait. There is no answer.

◊ *To fire at the figure, go to 29.*
◊ *To wait, go to 88.*

---

44 *Afternoon – 19 February 1945*
You shuffle forward to Tex and tell him that you have no choice but to check the pillbox. He nods in agreement.

The two of you lift yourselves out of the trench and stalk your way to the back of the pillbox. As you get near you can see that the defensive structure is built from reinforced concrete. You work your way to the rear of the pillbox and see a small entrance which has been scorched black. Lying on the floor, half in and half out of the doorway, is the charred remains of what you assume is an enemy soldier. He no longer looks human.

◊ *If you wish to check inside the pillbox, go to 2.*
◊ *If you wish to push forward, go to 92.*

Before you can react, Tex leans forward.

"How about we pick up some food at the same time we get the barbed wire?" he whispers.

A few minutes later, Tex, Mike and you are following the recently laid telephone cable back to Headquarters to get the barbed wire. You talk loudly; more scared of being shot by your own men than you are of the Japanese.

You arrive to find a pile of barbed wire bundles and a rather stressed Lieutenant. He returns your salute and orders you to take the wire – so much for getting something to eat. You lift a heavy roll of the metal wire onto your shoulder and start the journey back, talking loudly as you go.

You drop off the wire and then, at a crouching run, head back towards your crater. You are about one hundred metres from the shell hole when the first mortar lands. It impacts a few metres from your old blast hole. You throw yourself to the ground – Tex and Mike are close by. A second shell explodes directly in your old crater.

"Woah," says Tex. "I'm glad we went out for a walk now."

More mortar shells could land at any second.

◊ *To return to your old crater, which has just been hit, go to 53.*

◊ *To find a new shell hole, go to 10.*

Morning – 23 February 1945

The night passes without incident, but you barely sleep through the shelling, rifle fire and white flares. The morning skies have cleared and the rain has stopped – you feel quite refreshed.

You are preparing yourself for a lazy morning when a familiar figure stands at the lip of your shell hole. It is the Sergeant from the first day; his unlit cigar is still clamped between his teeth. You wonder if he ever plans to smoke it.

"Since you are both still alive," he growls, "I am rewarding you with a trip up there." He points to the mountain. "Now go and report in to the forward command post."

You and Mike quickly prepare and head to the command post tent. When you arrive, a group of six other Marines are standing around. You are just joining the group when an officer appears.

"OK," he barks. "It seems the Japs have given up on Suribachi. I want you to split into two groups and take a wander up to the summit to see what's what."

The Marines split into two groups. Which group will you and Mike join?

◊ *If you wish to join the first group, go to 91.*
◊ *If you wish to join the second group, go to 38.*

You are confident that the group behind will spot the Japanese soldier hiding out, so you push onwards. The path continues to wind upwards, but you are unable to relax. The rock-strewn mountainside offers just too many hiding places for the enemy.

The path twists close to a cave entrance and you are suddenly aware of the sound of shuffling feet. You raise your hand to stop the other Marines. They also listen – Mike turns to you and nods his head. As you watch he steps towards the cave and ducks into the darkness. You follow.

It takes a moment for your eyes to adjust to the darkness, but you can see a small cave. It is dry and cool, though a familiar sweet smell lingers in the air. There are two narrow tunnels leading from the cave.

◊ *If you wish to follow the left-hand tunnel, go to 75.*
◊ *If you wish to follow the right-hand tunnel, go to 85.*

With a smile Mike points towards the Sherman tank and then is off, disappearing from your view as he picks his way through the black rocks. You are quick to follow, bobbing from one rock to the next, careful not to expose yourself to Japanese snipers.

When you arrive at the tank you can see a number of Marines have had a similar idea. They have massed behind the tank and wait nervously for it to begin moving. You join them, quickly finding Mike.

The tank's advance is slow – the rough ground, black rocks and clumps of bushes making the progress difficult. As it chugs forward, it draws gunfire from the enemy. Its cannon sporadically bursts into action, blasting pillboxes and clearing away the enemy.

The ground begins to rise as you climb the mountainside. Rocks are larger and more difficult for the tank to navigate. As the tank's advance grinds to a halt, a skinny Lieutenant appears and directs you to attack beyond the tank.

Reluctantly, you move ahead, quickly finding safety behind a large jagged, black rock. Ahead of you are five Marines, also hidden in the cover of the rocks. They are laying down fire on an unseen enemy position. You can hear the distant machine gun that is pinning down the Marines ahead.

An hour passes and no progress is made. The Sun is hanging low in the sky and the light is beginning to fade. Finally, the skinny officer appears a few metres behind your position, and shouts for you to withdraw.

◊   *Go to 28.*

You have no time to think – the officer is moving so quickly he is upon you in an instant. As he brings the sword down towards your face, you step backwards and try to block the sword. The blade comes down and you grab his warm hands. He is weak and you wrestle the sword from his grasp.

You bring up the handle of the sword and smash it into the officer's nose. He staggers backwards. You dive for the floor and scoop up your M1 Garand. The officer is dazed and blood pours from his broken nose. You level the rifle and fire once. The office slumps to the ground and doesn't move.

The rest of the night passes without incident, and as the first light peeps over the horizon it starts to rain. You take your green poncho from your backpack, heaving it on over your uniform. You then make your way back to the forward command tent.

This time the tent has a different officer present. He is standing in the rain drinking coffee.

"Ahh," he says, "isn't it a great day to be alive." You guess you're not supposed to answer.

"I've got two jobs, so you can take your pick. The engineers on the beach need a hand unloading some supplies or you can wait with the other

Marines. They have formed a reserve just in case it
is needed to support today's attack."

◊ *If you want to help at the beach, go to 62.*

◊ *If you want to wait in the reserves, go to 31.*

Morning – 19 February 1945

50

You contemplate digging into the hot sand – your
training suggests you should – but you are tired
and seem to be at little risk. Instead, you relax in
your position and take the opportunity to sip from
your water canteen.

Minutes pass, and no orders come. A shout of
"incoming" drifts across the sand, and a thud some
distance to your left is followed by an explosion
and a shower of sand. A second explosion is closer,
and a third lands just a metre away. The blast
lifts you from the sand and sends you tumbling
backwards through the air. For a moment the
world goes black…

When you come round, pain shoots through
your body. You are lying on your back; your
helmet and weapons have gone. You look down
to where your left arm should be, but it's missing.
Your blood seeps into the sand.

You lie back and scream for a corpsman, but it's
the last thing you ever say or hear.

◊ *Sadly, you have been killed by your own artillery.*
Go to 98 to discover your fate.

51 *Morning – 19 February 1945*
With no other option, you spring to your feet, tuck
the BAR onto your right hip and run.

The first few metres pass in a blur. Adrenaline
keeps your legs pumping and for a moment you
think you might just make it – then the Japanese
machine gun spits back into life. You watch as the
gun swings in your direction; spurts of black sand
spouting at your feet.

You squeeze the trigger of the BAR and bullets
jolt from the gun, before you are hit. The first bullet
slams into your left leg, sending you crashing
towards the sand. The second and third bullets
do the real damage; one entering just above your
hip bone and ricocheting off your spine, the other
passing through your chest and heart. You slam
into the sand, already dead.

◊ *The wrong choice has cost you your life. Go to 98*
to discover your fate.

---

52 *Night – 19 February 1945*
You lift yourself onto one knee and fire off two
quick shots into the darkness. Just as you do, a
flare fizzes into life high above your head and you
are bathed in white light. Standing about twenty
metres away is a Japanese soldier. He is wearing
a brown uniform and has a black moustache. In
one hand is a rifle with a bayonet, in the other he

holds a grenade. Before you can react he tosses the grenade in your direction.

The throw is weak and as you flatten yourself to the ground, the grenade explodes away from you. A second later you are on your feet. You look back towards the enemy soldier to see he is now just a few metres away. His bayonet is lowered in your direction and he is almost on top of you, his screams echoing in your ears.

◊ *To dive out of the way of the bayonet attack, go to 77.*
◊ *To meet the attack and try to kill the enemy soldier, go to 12.*

Night – 20 February 1945   **53**

Thinking of the old saying "lightning never strikes twice", you dive for your old shell hole. The recent mortar shell has made the hole deeper and, strangely, you feel safer.

A second later you realise two things. The first is that you are not safe, the second that the old saying was wrong.

As Tex, Mike and you hunker down in the sand, another mortar shell drops into your crater, ending all three lives in a flash of flame and burning-hot metal.

◊ *The wrong choice has cost you your life. Go to 98 to discover your fate.*

Morning – 21 February 1945

The attack begins when a young Lieutenant springs from a nearby crater, waves his Thompson sub-machine gun in the air and screams "Attack!" You are out of your hole a few seconds later; Tex and Mike are hot on your heels.

The ground ahead has few rocks to hide behind, but the bombardment created many handy craters. Some barbed wire – a few metres away – has been pulled back, allowing you to charge through. As soon as you are close enough, the enemy opens fire. They are positioned in trenches about a hundred metres ahead, and despite the bombing they are still putting up a fierce fight.

The man to your right is hit and falls. A second later the man to your left takes a bullet in the chin. Shouts of "Corpsman! Corpsman!" quickly mingle with the sounds of gunfire and explosions.

You start to panic and begin to turn – you want to run away. Behind you the faces of Tex and Mike remind you that you are all scared. You can't let them down – you are a Marine! So, you turn back towards the Japanese trench and keep on running.

Just ahead you spot a fresh crater.

◊ *To duck into the crater, go to 83.*
◊ *To keep going forward, go to 19.*

55 *Afternoon – 21 February 1945*

You explain to Mike that a quick attack on the pillbox will work. You convince him that since they won't be expecting just two men to attack, you might be able to catch them by surprise.

He just shrugs and says, "I'll cover you."

Mike finds a concealed location behind a jagged black rock and opens fire on the pillbox. You wait until the steady snap-snap-snap of his M1 fills the air and then, at a crouched run, you start forward.

You skip out from behind the covering rock and head to the left of the pillbox. You plan to get up close and then drop a grenade through the slit.

You only take another five paces before you are hit. You are stopped in your tracks and slump to the ground. You are dead before the rest of your unit can get close enough to help.

◊ *Your actions have cost you your life. Go to 84 to discover your fate.*

---

56 *Morning – 19 February 1945*

With bullets whizzing just above your head, and Japanese shells thudding into the beach, you feel you have to make yourself as safe as possible.

Shifting your weight, you place your M1 Garand rifle on the sand next to you. You then roll to your left and unfasten your fighting knife from its secure sheath on your belt. The cold handle feels comforting in your hand. You plunge the knife into the warm black sand, using the blade to start scraping away. You put all your effort into trying to dig a hole large enough for you to crawl into.

It doesn't take long to realise that as quickly as you make a hole in the sand, it is filled with more loose sand from the surrounding edges. You pause for a moment, sweat forming on your face.

Then there is a flash, and everything goes black.

When you come round, you are lying on your back, on the beach about ten metres from the sand dune. You look up to see Marines flooding past you, a few glance in your direction, horror filling their faces. You ask them to help, reaching up and grabbing at their boots as they pass. Then you look down to see that your legs are missing. It takes you a moment to realise, but you don't live long enough to feel any pain.

◊ *You have been killed on the beaches of Iwo Jima by a Japanese mortar shell. Go to 98.*

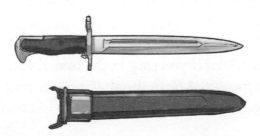

57 *Night – 20 February 1945*

In the dying light you take the chance to clean your M1 Garand. You have practised this a thousand times, and even in the dim light it is second nature. You flip over the rifle, remove the trigger section and lift the butt and stock cleanly off the barrel. You next remove the firing spring and firing mechanism, allowing you to discount the operating rod and firing bolt. You then carefully clean each item, making sure that no sand has become lodged in the delicate metal pieces. Once done, you reassemble the gun, testing all is well with a random shot into the darkness.

As you finish cleaning your rifle, a voice greets you from just outside the blast hole. You crawl on your belly towards the sound and find a Marine you don't recognise leaning in.

"We need someone to go back down the line and get some barbed wire. You interested in a little walk in the moonlight?"

◊ *To head back down to the beach to get the barbed wire, go to 45.*

◊ *If you would prefer to stay where you are, go to 80.*

---

58 *Morning – 21 February 1945*

You know that if you stay in the trench you will be well protected from the shelling – as long as the Japanese don't score a direct hit.

The explosions finally stop and you take the chance to look for Mike. You weave through the trenches, past injured Marines, until you finally spot your friend drinking from his canteen. Mike smiles and offers you a drink, then he tells you that you have been ordered to move out. You are to be part of an attack to secure the base of the mountain.

A few minutes later, your unit is moving past the trench complex and into the flat area behind it. You are right at the base of the mountain, which looms high above you, but the ground is not steep and there are many rocks and boulders to provide cover from Japanese snipers. As you advance, you duck down using the rocks as cover.

The rattle of a machine gun echoes out. Spurts of sand and chips of broken rock fly all around you. You hit the sand and roll behind the nearest rock. Peering over, about fifty metres away, you can see a well-hidden pillbox. The cone-shaped muzzle of a Japanese MG is pointing in your direction. You look backwards and realise that you have moved ahead of the other Marines in your unit. It will be a few minutes before they catch up.

◊ *To wait for the rest of your unit to arrive before attacking, go to 18.*

◊ *To convince Mike that a two-man attack on the pillbox is a good idea, go to 55.*

You hesitate for a moment and then scuttle to the bottom of the crater. The flame-thrower consists of a backpack that is made up of three joined tanks, each containing liquid napalm. You crouch down, fearful that lifting your head too high will result in a bullet ending your life. Once the backpack is in place you jiggle about to make it comfortable.

It is difficult to move with the flame-thrower on your back, but you soon crawl to the lip of the crater. Peeking over you see the wrecked pillbox. Glancing to your left and right, you ask your fellow Marines to give you covering fire. They immediately lay down gunfire against the pillbox, and after a few seconds the MG falls silent.

You seize the moment, lumbering forward like an over-packed donkey. The shifting sand and heavy weight on your back makes the going tough. With each lumbering step you pray that the Japanese MG will not start to fire again.

After what seems like for ever, you are about ten metres from the pillbox. You can see shapes ducking around in the gloom and waste no time in squeezing the trigger. A rod of orange flame springs from the hose, but your aim is off and it shoots high into the air above the pillbox. You keep your finger on the trigger, and direct the tongue of flame into the damaged pillbox slit. Black smoke billows from the napalm stream and the heat on your hands and cheeks is almost unbearable. You can hear nothing beyond the roar of the fire.

After about ten seconds the flame dies. You squeeze the trigger – nothing. The pillbox is flaming and the MG has stopped. You stagger back to the crater, flopping gratefully into the black sand. You lie on your back as you remove the flame-thrower and retrieve your M1 rifle.

◊ *Go to 42.*

Morning – 19 February 1945

It is not long before the word spreads that the Marines around you are about to advance. You wait until a few young Marines have formed into a line just ahead of where you are lying and then rush forward to fall in next to them. You recognise one of the group, he was on the same ship as you, but you can't remember his name.

You begin to advance through the sand. It rises and falls ahead of you, making it impossible to see more than a few hundred metres at most. Black rocks and wiry bushes are dotted in the sand. To the left, Mount Suribachi continues to provide the enemy with a stronghold to bombard the beaches.

You advance slowly and with caution, until you find yourself on a flat section of sand. You take cover amongst some rocks. Ahead of you, about one hundred metres away, is the black slit of a pillbox. About fifty Marines have now collected in the rocks, but the pillbox remains silent.

With your M1 Garand resting in your hand, you take aim at the pillbox. Suddenly the Japanese machine gun inside springs to life, and bullets zip through the air. Marines take cover and return fire.

◊ *If you wish to try to lead an attack on the pillbox, go to 90.*

◊ *If you wish to sit and wait for orders, go to 3.*

You push on along the trenches towards Mount Suribachi. As you get closer, the ground rises until you are finally at the base of the mountain.

You are given orders to move forward and plug a gap in the line. It is explained that a "call and counter-call" system is in place. If you think you see an enemy soldier in the darkness, call out the name of a US car. If he shouts a different US car name back, great; if not, then shoot to kill.

You move forward once the Sun has set and quickly find your place in the front line. The ground is rocky and digging in is impossible, so instead you position yourself between two rocks.

You are soon very cold, and every few minutes the darkness is illuminated by a bright, airborne flare. These are like huge fireworks attached to small parachutes; they float down from the sky bathing the area in a ghostly white light.

The night drags on. Occasionally the rattle of gunfire echoes out from the night. Another flare lights up the rocky ground ahead, and as it fades you see movement.

You shout out "Ford". A split second later comes back the word "Studebaker".

◊ *If you think it is a Japanese soldier and you want to open fire, go to 7.*

◊ *If you think it is a US Marine, hold fire and go to 95.*

Morning – 22 February 1945

You pick your way down to the beach as the rain continues to fall. Though it is still not totally safe, most of the enemy have been pushed away from the beach area.

The work on the beach is tough. The never-ending rain means that you can't remove your poncho, but as you lift boxes from ships onto the sand you quickly build up a sweat.

Occasionally, a Japanese mortar shell falls onto the beach and explodes in a shower of sand and debris, but otherwise the day passes smoothly as you are caught up in your own thoughts.

As the Sun sets, you meet up with Mike. He has dug out a bomb crater, fastened a green poncho to four sticks and created a dry tented area. The rain has eased and you look forward to some well-earned sleep.

◊ *Go to 46.*

Morning – 23 February 1945

You have come this far and it seems a shame not to go all the way to the top. You pick your way up to the summit and then stand admiring the view that greets you. Stretching out on all sides is the Pacific Ocean. Closer to the island, hundreds of black dots bob at anchor. Occasionally a flash and plume of smoke indicates that a battleship has fired onto the island. Only from this height do you get a sense of how small Iwo Jima really is.

◊ *If you wish to return to the forward command tent at the base of the mountain, go to 76.*

◊ *If you wish to make sure it is safe for more troops to come up, go to 41.*

Morning – 21 February 1945

You continue to race forward – you are breathing hard. Tex and Mike push past you. They weave to the left to avoid a crater and you do the same. Suddenly the ground dips slightly and you see that just ahead is a small pillbox. It is buried in the sand with just the black slit showing. Sandbags and rocks are stacked up on either side, leaving an easy route to the flat roof. Mike slips and falls in the black sand, while Tex manages to leap up and onto the roof of the pillbox.

◊ *To dive for cover next to Mike, go to 23.*

◊ *To join Tex on the roof of the pillbox, go to 71.*

65 *Morning – 19 February 1945*

You slowly examine the satchel of explosives. You recognise it as an M37 Demolition Kit. The bag contains explosives that are detonated by a small trigger which is attached by a long, thin wire. You prepare the explosives, take a deep breath, say a short prayer and climb over the lip of the crater.

The black slit of the pillbox is only about twenty-five metres away, and the machine gun is firing far to your right. You put your head down, pump your legs and zigzag as you run. God must be with you, because by the time the enemy spot you, you are already at the pillbox.

You slide to the ground and huddle against the wall. You can hear the splutter of the MG just above your head. Between bursts of gunfire you can also hear men talking in what you assume is Japanese.

◊ *If you wish to blow up the pillbox, go to 4.*
◊ *If you want to save the demolition kit and instead fire your BAR into the slit, go to 89.*

---

66 *Morning – 21 February 1945*

The morning light brings a shock. As you peer over the lip of your shell crater you see that you are just one hundred metres from the steep mountainside of Suribachi. The ground ahead is crisscrossed with trenches, though it is clear of rocks and bushes. A couple of bullets whizz overhead and you quickly duck down. An attack over this open ground will be virtually impossible.

You shift your position to keep a lookout. You count about twenty-five Japanese soldiers running along the trenches. They are crouched down but their shoulders and heads are still exposed. You bring up your M1 Garand and fire off a couple of quick shots. Tex and Mike are soon next to you, and also fire on the enemy. It is not long before more gunfire erupts into life from the craters all around. The Japanese soldiers disappear from view as quickly as they appeared.

The word soon spreads that you will be attacking across the open ground at 8:25. As the words sink in, you feel your stomach tighten. The minutes tick by and the moment of the attack draws closer. Shells from US artillery start to rain down on the trenches just a few hundred metres ahead of you. You duck into your crater.

There are just a few minutes to go before the planned attack, when Mike shuffles over next to you. He leans in close and asks if he can borrow your bayonet. He explains that he lost his.

◊ *If you wish to give Mike your bayonet, go to 6.*
◊ *If you wish to keep your bayonet, go to 33.*

Morning – 20 February 1945

You move cautiously out of the crater, taking just a few steps forward before ducking behind the nearest rock. Though bullets whizz about, none seem to be aimed at you, so you push on again, weaving past a bush and slipping behind a large black rock. Tex and Mike are close by. Then you are up on your feet again, M1 Garand in hand and sprinting for a crater. You dive in, wait a moment and then peek over the lip of the crater. The second your head pops up you hear a crack and a spout of sand jumps up in front of your face. Sniper!

You shuffle along the crater a metre or so and look again. Just ahead of you are some rocks. Next to the rocks is a dense mass of bushes and behind these you spot a narrow black opening in the mountainside – it must be a cave. Suddenly you see a flash of light and a bullet whizzes just over your head.

You drop into the crater, position your M1 Garand and once again peer over the lip.

You are sure the flashes came from just ahead, but where will you concentrate your aim?

◊ *If you wish to target the cave entrance, go to 87.*
◊ *If you wish to target the bushes, go to 8.*
◊ *If you think the sniper is amongst the rocks, go to 27.*

You pass the word down the line that you will investigate. You shift yourself away from the path and edge towards the cave entrance, ducking from rock to rock, M1 Garand at the ready. After days of fighting it is suddenly very quiet and you find yourself nervously creeping towards the darkness.

You are only a couple of metres from the cave when you spot a shape creeping away into the gloom. You take one step forward and shoulder your rifle. You are just about to fire when something lands at your feet. You glance down and see a grenade.

You just have time to take a few steps backwards before it explodes. The blast rips through your lower body and throws you in the air. The last sensation you have is of flying.

◊ *The Battle of Iwo Jima is over for you. Go to 84 to discover your fate.*

69 *Afternoon – 21 February 1945*

You have no intention of helping the enemy. You shake your head and stand up, leaving the Japanese soldier trapped. As you are about to move away, a group of three Marines appears. They come over to you, see the man and laugh.

One of the Marines, a tall man with thick stubble, pulls out his water canteen and sits next to the Japanese soldier.

"Thirsty?" he says, waving the bottle just above the trapped man's head. The enemy soldier nods. "Me too," says the Marine. With this he takes a huge swig of water and then laughs.

At this moment a corpsman arrives. With a wave of his hand he scatters the group of Marines and you move away.

◊ *Go to 81.*

---

70 You did it – but at a cost. Every day your scars will remind you of the horrors you suffered on the island of Iwo Jima.

You saw some of the most intense fighting that the US Marine Corp has ever experienced. Above all you showed the instincts of a Marine to survive, but the memories will haunt you forever...

◊ *Now go to 93 to see what happened in the real Battle of Iwo Jima.*

You scramble up on the flat roof next to Tex.

Behind the pillbox is a complex of trenches and from your slightly raised position you can see Japanese soldiers scurrying about below. They are surprised as you and Tex open fire.

Then, to your horror, you see the dark round shape of a grenade arcing through the air. It bounces once on the edge of the roof and rolls to a stop at your feet.

When the grenade explodes it will probably kill you and Tex.

◊ *If you wish to dive backward and hope you are quick enough to avoid the blast, go to 99.*

◊ *If you wish to sacrifice your own life to save Tex by diving on the grenade, go to 16.*

---

72 *Morning – 20 February 1945*

You watch from the safety of the tank as Tex and Mike weave their way through the rocky sand, finally diving into the crater. Gunfire is coming from all directions. As you pause, even more shots "ping" off the tank as you hear the distinctive stutter of a Japanese machine gun start firing to your left.

You consider your next move carefully. As you peer around the side of the tank you expose your head to the enemy. A sniper bullet passes cleanly through your helmet, entering your skull, killing you instantly.

◊ *Your moment of indecision has cost you your life. Go to 84 to discover your fate.*

Morning – 19 February 1945
You are just about to refuse when the Sergeant
steps forward and thrusts a slip of paper into the
hands of a Marine who is crouched in the sand
behind you. You breathe a sigh of relief.

Minutes pass. The occasional burst from the
distant machine gun keeps you close to the sand,
but on the whole you feel pretty safe. The Marines
about you seem to be waiting for orders before
they move on.

◊ *If you wish to dig into the sand to make your position
safer, go to 11.*

◊ *If you don't want to waste time digging in, go to 50.*

Morning – 20 February 1945
After a word with Tex and Mike, you decide a
simple charge will be best. The plan is to spring
forward, lob a few grenades and run into the
crater. It takes a few minutes for you to prepare,
but finally you are ready.

You take two steps out of the crater, and then
pause as you pull the pin out of a grenade; Tex
and Mike have done the same. You bring the
grenade up to throw when you are hit in the arm.
The bullet grazes your skin, slicing your uniform,
but you drop the grenade. Screaming to Tex and
Mike, you dive to the left. As you hit the ground,
the grenade goes off at the feet of your friends. You

watch helplessly as they are blown into the air.

The Japanese soldiers in the crater ahead now target you on the ground. Your ears are ringing, and you try to crawl back to the shell hole. Bullets pass through your body, tearing muscle and piercing organs, until you finally stop crawling and die.

◊ *Tragically, the Battle of Iwo Jima is over for you and your friends. Go to 84 to discover your fate.*

---

75 *Afternoon – 23 February 1945*

You point to the left-hand tunnel and Mike nods. You bring your rifle up and creep forward. The tunnel is narrow and soon twists to the left. As you swing around the corner you see a Japanese soldier ducking out of sight and you fire a shot, which echoes in the darkness.

There is a bright flash and a shockwave throws you backwards as a grenade explodes at your feet. You land on your back, your ears pounding so much that you can't hear yourself screaming in agony. You clutch your smashed legs and Mike appears at your side, dragging you backwards towards the light outside.

◊ *The Battle of Iwo Jima is over for you. Though your wound is serious enough for a ticket home, you will survive this battle… Now go to 70 to discover your fate.*

With the mountain safe, you decide to head back to the forward command tent. You are still on your guard – looking out for enemy soldiers – but as you near the base of the slope you begin to relax. Ahead of you the path is strewn with boulders and Mike slows down to make sure it's not a trap.

As you wait, an explosion knocks you from your feet. You tumble down the track until a boulder brings you to a violent stop. Your body smashes against the rock and you black out. Some time later you wake up and slowly haul yourself up, screaming out in pain. One of your legs is broken and so is one of your arms. Mike is lying close by, his legs ripped and bloody. You try to dress Mike's wounds as best you can to stop him bleeding to death, before finally a corpsman arrives.

◊ *The Battle of Iwo Jima is over for you. Though your wound is serious enough for a ticket home, you will survive this battle... Now go to 70 to discover your fate.*

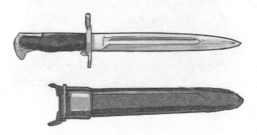

Night – 19 February 1945

You wait for a split second, watching the tip of the bayonet, and then roll to the right to avoid the initial thrust.

You are too slow. The blade nicks your arm as you fall, causing you to wince in pain. For a second you pause. The Japanese soldier – still screaming – stands over your body and plunges his bayonet into your stomach. You feel the cold steel enter, and then you splutter with further agony as the blade is twisted inside you. You lie in the darkness for a number of minutes, crying out for your mother, before your life finally slips away.

◊ *Your battle has ended with your agonising death. Go to 84 to discover your fate.*

You catch up with Tex, and after a few words, decide to ignore the burned-out pillbox. Tex then drops in behind you with Mike and you push on past the pillbox and along the trench.

As you creep past the blackened structure you hold your breath, but nothing happens. A few paces further on you are suddenly stopped in your tracks by a horrific sight. Lying in the trench, just a few paces ahead, is a severed leg. A white and grey sock, plus a brown army-issue boot, tell you the leg once belonged to a US Marine. You pause for a moment and then carry on.

The trench continues to weave to the left and right. The Marines ahead have now started to bunch up. You can't see what is holding up the line. Suddenly your face is sprayed with blood and the Marine in front of you slumps forward. A split second later you hear the crack of a rifle shot. You quickly throw yourself to the ground shouting "Sniper!" Crawling forward you see the Marine is dead. It appears a sniper's bullet has passed through his head. You check yourself for a wound – somehow the bullet missed you. You wipe the blood from your eyes, and then check that Tex and Mike are OK before ducking down and pushing onwards along the trench.

◊ *Go to 92.*

79 *Morning – 23 February 1945*

You and the other three Marines fan out with equal distance between each man. You move towards the location of the movement, ducking from rock to rock, making the most of the cover.

After a few minutes searching about, you find nothing. Then you hear noises to your right and the muffled sound of foreign voices. You see a narrow path weaving between two large boulders and you indicate to the men that you are going to investigate. They duck into cover and wait.

You edge forward, rifle ready, and follow the narrow path where you have to squeeze between two rocks. On the other side, hidden in a shallow dip in the rocks, are two enemy soldiers armed with a heavy machine gun. Before you can move the MG splutters to life, cutting you down where you stand.

◊ *The Battle of Iwo Jima is over for you. Go to 84 to discover your fate.*

---

80 *Night – 20 February 1945*

You send the Marine on his way, explaining that you have no intention of getting out of your safe shell hole. Still lying on your back you look up at the stars. You can hear the deep breathing of Tex and Mike, both of whom are asleep. Occasionally you hear a rifle going off in the dark, but it is somehow calmer than it was the night before, though flares still fizz into life, bathing your crater hole in white light.

You feel yourself drifting to sleep when you are jerked into life by an explosion. It has hit just outside your hole, the detonation sending sand in all directions. You are just about to move when a second mortar shell hits, landing at the back of your crater. For a split second you see the shell half buried in the sand, its grey metal smoking slightly. Then it explodes, killing you instantly.

◊ *You have been killed by a Japanese mortar shell – the Battle of Iwo Jima is over for you. Go to 84.*

Night – 21 February 1945

The night is closing in quickly. You scurry to the forward command post, only to find the hastily erected tent deserted apart from a flustered-looking officer. He doesn't even look up as you enter. You wait a moment and then leave. With little choice you pick your way through the nearby rocks. The wind is stronger and the temperature is dropping quickly. You find an area amongst the rocks that is protected from the weather and settle down for the night.

Your sleep is filled with strange dreams, from which you are regularly woken by the white flares and explosions in the night. One particularly close explosion wakes you, showering rock and sand down on you, and you can't get back to sleep.

The wind whistles through the rocks and though it is nearly morning, it is still cold and dark. Suddenly you spot a shape moving. You spring to your feet. Out of the darkness looms a Japanese soldier. He is dressed as an officer and wears a clean, crisp shirt and hat. As he races towards you he lifts a shiny samurai sword high into the air above his head and lets out a mighty scream.

◊ *To try to grab your rifle, go to 9.*
◊ *To try to block the sword, go to 49.*

Morning – 19 February 1945

As the confusion of the battle fills your mind, your training takes over. You know that the best way to avoid enemy fire is to find cover, and if there is no cover, then dig in.

You stumble forward across the black sand, the waves lapping up at your heels. Bullets from enemy machine-gun positions buzz through the air as you attempt to cross the open beach. Marines push up inland from the landing craft, stepping over the bodies of their fallen brothers-in-arms.

Somehow you reach the sand dune and drop to your knees. You start digging into the coarse sand with your hands. You have only pulled a few handfuls of the sand from the hole when you are hit. You feel a thump on your neck, and for a second you think you have been punched. Your hands instinctively lift up and you can feel your warm, sticky blood on your cold fingers. You try to get to your feet, but instead stagger backwards clutching at your throat. Then you fall to the sand, where you lie gazing up at the sky until finally light fades from your eyes.

◊ *You've been unlucky and have been killed on the beaches of Iwo Jima. You will need more luck to survive this battle. Go back to 1 to try again.*

You take two more steps and then dive into the crater, belly first. It is wide and shallow, and by the time Tex and Mike have joined you there is little room. Suddenly there is an explosion on the lip of the crater and the shockwaves from the blast buffet your body. Your ears ring and for a moment the whole world goes black.

A second later, Tex is by your side pointing to your head. Ducking down you remove your helmet to see a hole in the metal. Lifting your hand to your head you feel blood just above the ear. Tex leans in and examines the wound.

"Woah, you are sure a lucky boy – nothing but a scratch."

You thank him, kiss your helmet and plop it back onto your head.

◊ *If you wish to remain where you are, go to 14.*
◊ *If you wish to move forward with the rest of your unit, go to 64.*

84 You survived for almost the whole of the initial battle, which is better than many Marines who died on the beaches of Iwo Jima. US Marines came up against fierce resistance and were under constant attack – just one wrong choice could mean death.

If you are to survive this battle you need to forget a lot of what you learned in training and start listening to your instincts. Think carefully about your choices and keep your fingers crossed for a bit more luck.

◊ *Now go back to section 1 and give it another go…*

---

85 *Afternoon – 23 February 1945*

You point to the right-hand tunnel and Mike nods in agreement. You bring your rifle up and creep forward. The tunnel leads to a larger cave. You pause before entering, making sure that it is clear. As you step forward, the first thing that greets you is an intense sickly sweet smell. You then see where it is coming from.

Propped up against the wall of the cave is the body of a US Marine. You flash a look at Mike. His face is frozen in a look of horror. The dead Marine is covered in blood.

"What the—" Mike begins, but an ear-pounding explosion knocks you both off your feet, sending you smashing into the rock wall. When you come round your leg feels as though it's on fire. It's badly damaged, but you can still put your weight on it. A wound to your stomach seeps blood through your jacket, and forces you to hunch over. Mike's right leg is mangled. You tie a tourniquet around his calf using your belt, and begin to drag your friend back down the tunnel towards the daylight outside.

◊ *The Battle of Iwo Jima is over for you. Though your wound is serious enough for a ticket home, you will survive this battle… Now go to 70 to discover your fate.*

Morning – 19 February 1945

You close your eyes, and for a second think of home. You then glance around the small black rock, count to three and run.

The first couple of steps are made before the Japanese can react. Your booted feet slip and slide in the shifting black sand, and you struggle to pick up any real speed. You are heading back the way you have come – up and over a small hump in the sand. If you can make it to the other side, the Japanese soldiers in the pillbox will not be able to see you.

Suddenly the rattle of the machine gun sends sand spitting up at your feet, and the fizz of bullets in the air around your ears. You first zig to the right, and then zag to the left, all the time pumping your legs.

With a final superhuman effort, you leap over the lip of the sand and roll into the safety behind. The MG falls silent.

You wait for a couple of minutes to regain your breath. You have no idea which way to go, and set off to your right. After a few minutes you see the shapes of some Marines lying in a shell crater. You jog up to their position and slump down into their hole.

◊ *Go to 60.*

You try to control your breathing as you aim at the black slit in the distant rock face. Your finger hovers on the trigger as you peer along the sights.

Then you spot a slight movement and the shape of a Japanese soldier emerges from the darkness. Without hesitation you squeeze the trigger of the M1 Garand, the gun bucking as you fire. In the distance you see the soldier stop and slump to the ground. You sink back into the crater and indicate to Tex and Mike that it is safe to move on.

Once again you are moving forward slowly, hopping from cover, ducking into shell holes and throwing yourself behind rocks. Though bullets whizz about your head, you rarely see any exposed enemy soldiers. They remain hidden, preferring to let off the odd shot and then disappear back into their tunnels and caves.

The Sun is dipping low in the sky, but you have managed to move close to the base of Mount Suribachi. The mountain looms high above your head, almost blocking out the light. You find yourself in yet another crater; it is wide and shallow, far from ideal cover. You signal to your two comrades that they should move forward, when the stutter of a Japanese machine gun fills the air. There's nowhere to go – the MG has you pinned down.

It is almost dark when the MG finally falls silent and, before you can move, word is passed from Marine to Marine that you are to bed in for the night.

◊ *If you want to take this chance to clean the sand from your rifle before trying to get some sleep, go to 57.*

◊ *If you want to try to find a better shell hole for the night, go to 43.*

---

88 *Night – 20 February 1945*

You wait just to make sure, staring into the darkness. At first you see nothing, then just ahead, you spot the shape of a crouched figure. You can tell from his helmet that it is an enemy soldier. He is about ten metres away and hasn't seen you. Carefully you take aim and when you are sure you will hit him, you pull the trigger. Click! Your rifle jams. You fumble with the bolt, trying to clear the jam.

You feel a bullet slam into your neck before you hear the shot. You fall back down. Tex fires his rifle into the darkness, while Mike pushes your hand against your throat, calling "Corpsman!" But you've seen wounds like this, and you quickly pass from this world with a prayer on your lips.

◊ *Your dirty rifle has cost you your life. Go to 84 to discover your fate.*

At the last moment you decide to save the explosives and instead use the BAR. You drop the satchel and release the denoting wire, switching to the large rifle so that it is ready to fire. You wait a moment and then spring to your feet.

Above your head is the narrow black slit, through which you can see two Japanese soldiers crouching in the gloom. You poke the muzzle of your rifle into the darkness and pull the trigger. The "snap-snap-snap" of bullets is followed by flashes that light up the inside of the pillbox. You watch as the first soldier is thrown backwards by the force of the gunfire. However, the second soldier reacts quickly and ducks to the left, pulling out a small black pistol as he moves. You try to swing your gun to fire a second burst, but the barrel of the enemy machine gun blocks your way.

In a panic you try to drop to your knees, but you are too slow. With deadly accuracy the Japanese soldier fires a single shot from point-blank range. It whistles through the slit and enters your forehead just above your eyes, killing you instantly.

◊ *You didn't follow direct orders and have paid the ultimate price. Go to 98 to discover your fate.*

You feel that the best course of action is to react quickly. Though you have no orders to attack, and the pillbox is about a hundred metres away, you spring to your feet and scream to attack.

You emerge from the rocks like a demon possessed, and sprint at the pillbox. As you run you bring the M1 up to your shoulder and let off a few wild shots. The Japanese machine gun swings to meet your attack and with a single burst you are hit. The bullets rip into your shoulder and spin you to the ground. You struggle to remain awake but the pain causes you to slip into blackness...

You wake to see the face of a corpsman peering over you. You are on your back, and a blood-soaked bandage covers your wounded shoulder. The corpsman smiles at you. You realise you are on a stretcher, before you black out again...

When you come round you are on the beach in a line of stretchers, each with a wounded Marine on. Suddenly a huge explosion goes off near you. Hot sand and lethal shrapnel rip through the line of wounded Marines. You don't feel the red-hot piece of metal that flies through the air, and passes through your skull, killing you in an instant.

◊ *You should have waited for direct orders before carrying out the attack. Go to 98 to discover your fate.*

You join two other Marines to make a group of four. The other two Marines seem to know each other well, and are chatting as you join them – they barely look up as you introduce yourself.

It is not long before you set off up the mountain. You pick your way up the path, which rises steeply and twists around the side of the mountain. As the path rises the landscape changes, and you are unsettled by all the potential hiding places you see – the large rocks, outcrops and caves.

You nervously plod onwards. Suddenly the line stops and the Marine in front of you points to your left. You are not sure, but you think you see a shape duck behind a rock.

◊ *If you wish to fan out and investigate the movement, go to 79.*

◊ *If you wish to ignore the movement and keep moving go to 47.*

92 *Afternoon – 19 February 1945*

You plod onwards, crouching to make the most of the trench. A rough rock-strewn landscape stretches out to your left and right. Folds in the terrain and scraggy bushes make it impossible to see more than about one hundred metres. Dominating the landscape is Mount Suribachi to your left. The trenches all seem to be winding in the direction of the mountain.

You have seen many bodies as you have navigated through the trenches, but few wounded men. This now changes. In a twist in the trenches you stumble upon a Marine, sitting with his back to the trench wall. He is clutching a dirty bandage to his eyes, blood is streaked down his cheeks.

As you move closer, the blind Marine senses your presence.

"Help." His voice is no more than a strained whisper. "Help me."

◊ *If you wish to escort the Marine back towards the beaches to get medical help, go to 25.*

◊ *If you want to ignore the man, go to 61.*

---

93 On 26 March 1945, the Battle of Iwo Jima ended as US forces finally took control. It had lasted 36 days and cost 5,000 American and 20,000 Japanese lives.

The Japanese saw Iwo Jima as part of their homeland and were prepared to die before letting the Americans occupy it. Yet the small, black rock in the middle of the Pacific Ocean had great importance for the American battle plans. Though the island was small it did have an airstrip, which allowed huge American bombers to land, refuel and be repaired as they flew to attack the Japanese mainland. Even before the battle had ended, damaged bombers were landing on the airstrip, despite the fighting still going on all around them.

The Battle of Iwo Jima became famous for a picture that was taken of a flag being raised on the top of Mount Suribachi. This picture was seen on the front of newspapers all around the world, and even before the battle had ended, the Marines who had lifted the flag were flown off the island and taken back to the US as heroes.

To this day the Battle of Iwo Jima remains one of the Marines' greatest and most bloody memories.

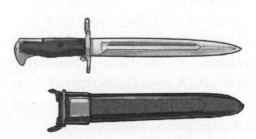

Morning – 19 February 1945

You are resisting the temptation to start digging, when a blast to your right causes you to be showered with black sand. You duck, instinctively, and you glance at the Marine who was digging. He has now stopped, and looking closely at his face, his staring eyes tell you that he is dead.

A figure appears next to you with the three stripes of a Sergeant on his arm.

"Marine," the Sergeant barks in your face. "Pick up that BAR and silence that god damn Jap MG." As he speaks, he pokes first at the dead Marine's gun, and then up and over the lip of the sand dune.

You scramble to pick up the Browning Automatic Rifle and crawl to the lip of the dune. Ahead you can see an open area, mostly flat black sand but studded with shell holes. Immediately ahead is the dark slit of an enemy pillbox. Spitting from the darkness is the muzzle of a Japanese machine gun. It is raking the dune, sending fire from left to right.

Still lying on your stomach, you drag the gun in front of you, prepare it to fire and pull the trigger. The gun bucks, shots spurting. The "snap-snap-snap" of the BAR sends jolts through your body. You see the bullets hitting the pillbox and for a second the Japanese MG stops firing.

Just as you relax the Sergeant reappears.

"Good work, Marine," he spits. "Now get up there and finish the job." As he speaks, he directs a number of Marines to lay down some cover fire. You have no choice but to attack the pillbox.

◊ *If you wish to run straight for the silenced pillbox, go to 51.*

◊ *If you wish to run forward and then jump into the nearest shell hole, go to 15.*

Night – 19 February 1945

You wait, finger on trigger. Then, emerging out of the gloom you see a figure. You are about to squeeze off a shot, when you recognise the shape of the helmet as that of a US Marine. A smiling face emerges from the darkness. He winks in your direction, but passes by you without a word.

You relax. The cold is now intense and you occasionally blow into your hands to keep your fingers warm. With each falling flare, you stare into the darkness to try to spot movement.

The night is wearing on, but you try to stay alert. As the latest flare fizzles above your head you are sure you can see movement.

You spit out the word "Ford".

Nothing…

◊ *If you wish to shoot into the darkness, go to 52.*

◊ *If you wish to wait, go to 22.*

With the morning comes a cup of coffee and a chance to grab some food. Just as you are sipping your hot drink a Sergeant you don't recognise shuffles past. He ducks down next to you and explains that you will be involved in the attack on the mountain, but you need to wait for tank support.

About an hour passes before you hear the squeak and rattle of two Sherman tanks. You watch as they plough though the loose sand, negotiating a route past burned-out pillboxes, and move into position just ahead of you. Suddenly hundreds of Marines pop up from cover all around and form a squad of troops behind each tank. You are one of the last to move, and quickly locate Tex and Mike. The tanks set off at a slow pace, the rumble of the tracks and the petrol fumes making it difficult to concentrate. It is not long before the tanks are drawing gunfire, bullets pinging off their armour.

You are heading towards the mountain, and though the ground is still sandy, there are now many rocks and bushes. The advance is slow and the constant fire from the enemy leaves you worried. Every now and then the tanks stop, the mighty gun turrets swing round and blast enemy pillboxes, and even tanks that the Japanese have dug into the sand. Smoke clouds the sky as the tanks create a trail of destruction. Yet, as the ground gets steeper, the tanks slow down even more, until the word spreads that the tanks can't go any further.

Tex moves in close to you and points out from behind the tank to a nearby crater.

◊ *If you wish to follow Tex into the crater, go to 36.*
◊ *If you want to wait a moment to see what happens, go to 72.*

Morning – 19 February 1945

You spring to your feet like an excited school boy. You weave between the black rocks and prone Marines, dodging machine-gun bullets and kicking up sand as you run. Within just a couple of minutes you are behind the square tank. Petrol fumes billow from the tank's exhaust and the noise is deafening. You race to the front of the tank and peer into the narrow slit of the driver. A smiling face greets you out of the gloom. You lift your hand to the side of your head to do an impression of speaking on the phone. You then scramble to the rear of the tank.

The phone is enclosed in a small metal box and you must wait for a red light to flash before the crew inside can hear you speak. You wait – nothing happens. Then a red flash. You swing open the door and whip out the phone, pushing the "speak" button.

"Howdy," says a muffled voice. You shout into the phone over the noise of battle, explaining that their fire is too far to the right, and suggest they correct by about two metres.

You replace the phone and move away as the tank fires its cannon. The shell impact is too far to the left of the pillbox. The MG is only silenced for a moment. You scuttle back to the phone, the light is flashing.

"Any good?" says the voice. You tell them to correct to the right by one metre. Once again you get out of the way of the tank and watch safely as the tank's cannon sends a shell right into the mouth of the pillbox. An explosion follows. When the smoke and sand clear, the pillbox is gone; in its place is a mound of rubble.

You jog back to your position with claps and cheers ringing in your ears. Crouching behind a rock, you wait for the next orders.

◊ *Go to 13.*

It is not that you are a bad solider, it is just that you are unlucky. More US Marines died on the beaches and rocks of Iwo Jima than any other place on Earth. The battle was bloody and hard fought, with many survivors simply describing Iwo Jima as "hell".

If you are to survive this battle you need to think carefully about your choices and keep your fingers crossed for a bit more luck.

◊ *Now go back to section 1 and give it another go…*

99

Morning – 21 February 1945

With one quick step backwards, you dive from the pillbox roof. Just as you leap, the grenade explodes. The force pushes you through the air and you land in a heap a metre or so from the pillbox roof. It takes you a couple of minutes to regain your senses – all the time, bullets whizz past your body.

Looking up you can see the crumpled remains of Tex on the roof. You rise to go to him, but as you do Mike grabs you by the arm, telling you to leave him. You obey.

You lie face down in the sand for a few moments, grief and guilt wracking your body. Then, with little option, you look up. Marines now flood past you on all sides. You are dragged to your feet by unseen hands to join the attack.

The complex of trenches spreads out in front of you; the pillbox squats to your right. The trenches are about waist high. You drop into the nearest one and look about. To your left and right Marines flood into the complex and spread out.

Over the trenches ahead you can see Japanese soldiers running about. You drop to one knee and fire off a few shots, but they seem to have little effect. You then realise that the Japanese are flooding into the area, too. Looking carefully, you can see enemy soldiers appearing from nearby cave entrances and hiding holes. They are going to try to fight back!

◊ *If you wish to continue to fire your M1 Garand into the massing Japanese troops, go to 21.*

◊ *If you wish to throw a couple of grenades, go to 34.*

---

100 *Morning – 23 February 1945*

You are about to speak when Mike pipes up.

"The Japs are all hiding; just leave 'em." You nod in agreement.

You can see the other four Marines ahead of you. Your group continues to climb up the path as it turns. It is difficult to see further than a few metres ahead as rocks and bushes block your view, but despite this, the climb is easy, if nerve-wracking.

As you near the summit of the mountain you see the other group of Marines are already there. They seem relaxed, three of them standing, whilst the fourth is peeing against a nearby rock.

◊ *If you feel your job is done and you wish to return to the forward command post, go to 39.*

◊ *If you want to go all the way to the top, go to 63.*

BATTLE BOOKS
BEHIND THE SCENES

The author: GARY SMAILES

I decided to write the Battle Books series after becoming really annoyed that someone had not already got off their backsides and written them for me. You see, battles are just so great to read about – all the weapons and action – in fact, I don't understand why there aren't more books about them…

I live on the Wirral, which many years ago was inhabited by real-life Vikings. Sometimes, when I'm writing and I get stuck, I go out for a walk with my (stinky) dog. I imagine I'm part of a Viking army defending my land.

If I could have three wishes, one would be that I was a Viking, and the other would be to own a Viking longboat. The third would be that my dog didn't smell so much!

The artist: DAVID COUSENS

I'm David, and I drew the artwork in *Battle Books: Iwo Jima*. I do a lot of work producing tutorials for budding illustrators, which are featured in magazines. Drawing something like *Battle Books: Iwo Jima* is great because it's not every day that someone asks you to draw battle illustrations.

ROUGH   FINAL

The piece above is from paragraph 20. I use photographic references to make sure I capture all the details, but I don't include all of these at the rough stage. You can see in this rough that I've just drawn the shape of a tank as a guide to position. Once this has been approved, I add in all the Sherman tank details, including the tracks and shading on the armour. In this piece, I was asked to change the position of the Marine and to make sure he was holding his rifle.

Finished reading Iwo Jima and survived?
There are more titles in the
Battle Books series to get stuck into...

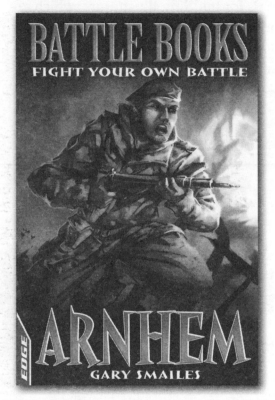

It is 1944, and Europe is still in the iron claw of Nazi
German forces. Allied forces have landed in Normandy,
and now British leaders have a plan to drop elite
troops deep into occupied Europe to capture key
targets, including bridges.
You are a Lieutenant in the 2nd Parachute Battalion.
Your choices will decide if your men make it through
enemy territory to reach the bridge in Arnhem. Then
you must capture and hold the bridge, at any cost...

"History does not get any more exciting than this."

Terry Deary, author of *HORRIBLE HISTORIES*, talking about *Battle Books*

It is 490 BCE and the ancient city of Athens is under threat. The Persians have sailed across the ocean to invade your land, and now camp on the plains of Marathon, just a few miles from Athens.

You are Miltiades, an old warrior with one last chance to prove your loyalty to the city you love. You command the mighty Greek Hoplite army, and your choices will decide if you can halt the Persian invasion and save Athens...

BATTLE BOOKS

Take up your weapons and prepare to fight your own battle...

978 1 4451 0112 5

978 1 4451 0113 2

978 1 4451 0114 9

978 1 4451 0115 6